CATCH A DINOSAUR

AND OTHER PREHISTORIC BEASTS

Susan Hayes

Consultant: Dr Neil DL Clark
Hunterian Museum, University of Glasgow

CONTENTS

There are DINOSAURS
and other prehistoric beasts in this book!

SOMEONE left the door OPEN. The door to another dimension, where time is all MIXED UP. And before anyone noticed, a medley of PREHISTORIC CREATURES got through!

They stomped and they roared. They gnashed their teeth. They swung their tails. They raised their horns. *Spinosaurus*, *TYRANNOSAURUS REX*, *Velociraptor*, *Diplodocus*, *TRICERATOPS*, *Quetzalcoatlus*, *MEGALODON*, *Smilodon*, and many MORE entered OUR WORLD.

BUT then a strange thing happened. The beasts dissolved into thin air. Their ROARS could still be heard, and the ground still SHOOK, but it wasn't until darkness fell that they became apparent.

Darkness is NO CLOAK for these mighty, ferocious, and EXTRAORDINARY beasts. In the dark, they can hide no longer. Instead, they shine and glow like beacons of the night.

You must CATCH them!

At the moment the dinosaurs and prehistoric creatures are hiding in different places in **THIS** book. It is your job to find them, keep an eye on them, and make sure they don't escape again. ALL YOU HAVE TO DO IS—

1. Study the BEAST
2. Look at the CLUES
3. Find the HABITAT
4. Turn out the LIGHTS

When you find each beast, if they glow brightly, we are all safe. DO NOT let them ESCAPE! They are DANGEROUS in the outside WORLD—to themselves, to you, and most definitely to any cute fluffy PETS.

PLEASE!!

DO NOT tip the book upside down. DO NOT shake it. DO NOT leave the room with the book OPEN. And DO NOT use it to swat flies or scare your little brother or sister.

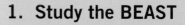

5

How do you CATCH a DINOSAUR?

It's simple. Just study the CLUES, find the HABITAT, and turn out the LIGHTS. To make sure you've found all the dinosaurs and prehistoric creatures, check page 48.

How to catch SPINOSAURUS

1. Study the CLUES

These CLUES will help you to find where SPINOSAURUS is hiding in this book:

Each beast has its own CLUES box. Study it carefully.

Spinosaurus can SWIM, it hunts CROCODILES, and catches FISH to eat. Which habitat do you think it's hiding in?

forest
desert
swamp
city
park
ocean
tundra
savanna

 Paddle-like feet tell us that *Spinosaurus* swims. Find water.

 Razor-sharp teeth mean meat-eating. Look for prey, such as crocodiles.

 Super sharp claws for catching slippery fish. Look for *Spinosaurus*'s favorite food.

 Now turn to the GLOW-IN-THE-DARK habitat pages to catch a *SPINOSAURUS*!

There is MORE information on the *Spinosaurus* page that can help you, too:

WHEN *SPINOSAURUS* lived 100 million years ago, it stalked the giant swamps of North Africa.

2. Find the HABITAT

Did you find fish, water, and crocodiles in the SWAMP?

Spinosaurus "will eat just about any meat." It is likely that it will prey on panthers, too.

REMEMBER!
All the dinosaurs and the other prehistoric creatures must EAT. They will look for a habitat that provides them with FOOD.

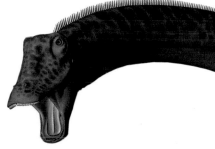

3. Turn off the LIGHTS

What else is HIDING in the SWAMP?

The giant crocodile, *Saurosuchus*, and the fish-eating pterosaur, *Zhenjiangopterus*.

When you turn out the lights, *SPINOSAURUS* will appear.

It will GLOW in the DARK.

Are you READY to catch the other BEASTS?

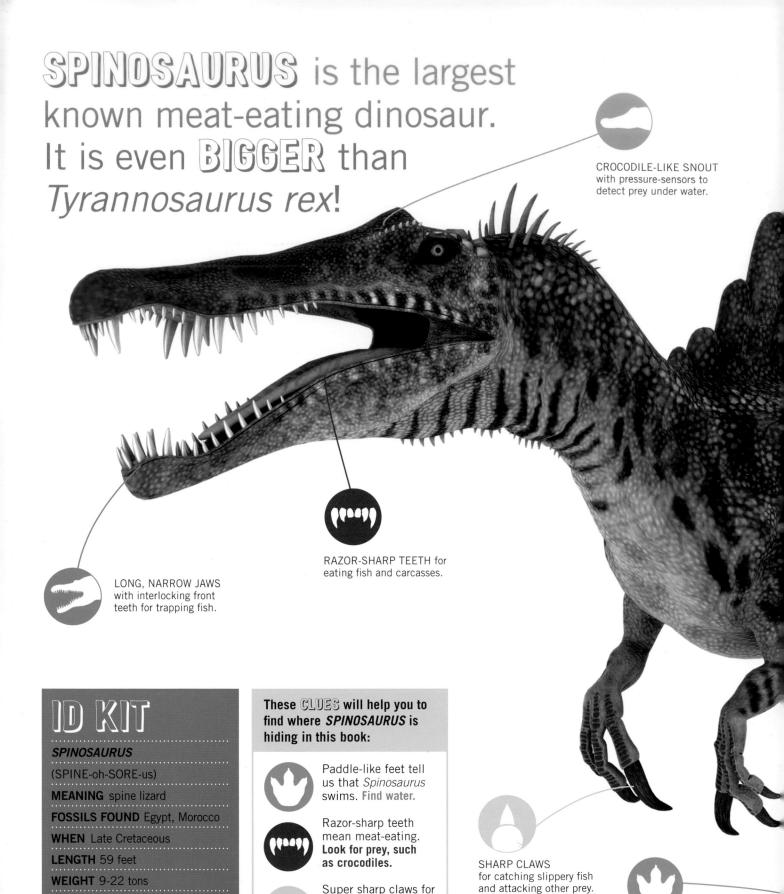

SPINOSAURUS is the largest known meat-eating dinosaur. It is even **BIGGER** than *Tyrannosaurus rex*!

CROCODILE-LIKE SNOUT with pressure-sensors to detect prey under water.

RAZOR-SHARP TEETH for eating fish and carcasses.

LONG, NARROW JAWS with interlocking front teeth for trapping fish.

SHARP CLAWS for catching slippery fish and attacking other prey. *Spinosaurus* will eat just about any meat.

PADDLE-SHAPED FEET for moving through water easily.

ID KIT

SPINOSAURUS

(SPINE-oh-SORE-us)

MEANING spine lizard

FOSSILS FOUND Egypt, Morocco

WHEN Late Cretaceous

LENGTH 59 feet

WEIGHT 9-22 tons

DIET carnivore

FOOD fish, eggs, meat

These **CLUES** will help you to find where *SPINOSAURUS* is hiding in this book:

Paddle-like feet tell us that *Spinosaurus* swims. **Find water.**

Razor-sharp teeth mean meat-eating. **Look for prey, such as crocodiles.**

Super sharp claws for catching slippery fish. Look for *Spinosaurus*'s favorite food.

Now turn to the GLOW-IN-THE-DARK habitat pages to catch a *SPINOSAURUS*!

HUGE SAIL may be used to scare off predators, attract mates, or control body temperature.

THIS DINOSAUR CAN SWIM! *Spinosaurus* has flat, paddle-like feet, perfect for wading through water. Its nostrils are on top of its nose like a crocodile, so it can breathe when partly submerged. Its huge body, with its long neck and tail and 7-foot-tall sail can move more easily in water than on land.

FISH provide *Spinosaurus* with an energy-filled snack. This beast lives and hunts in water and on the land, just like a modern-day crocodile.

DENSE BONES (simliar to modern-day penguins' and sea cows' bones) to help buoyancy in water.

WHEN *SPINOSAURUS* lived 100 million years ago, it stalked the giant swamps of North Africa. It was a dangerous place, full of huge dinosaurs, giant pterosaurs, and super-sized crocodiles.

VELOCIRAPTOR
is small, intelligent, and FEROCIOUS. It hunts in PACKS.

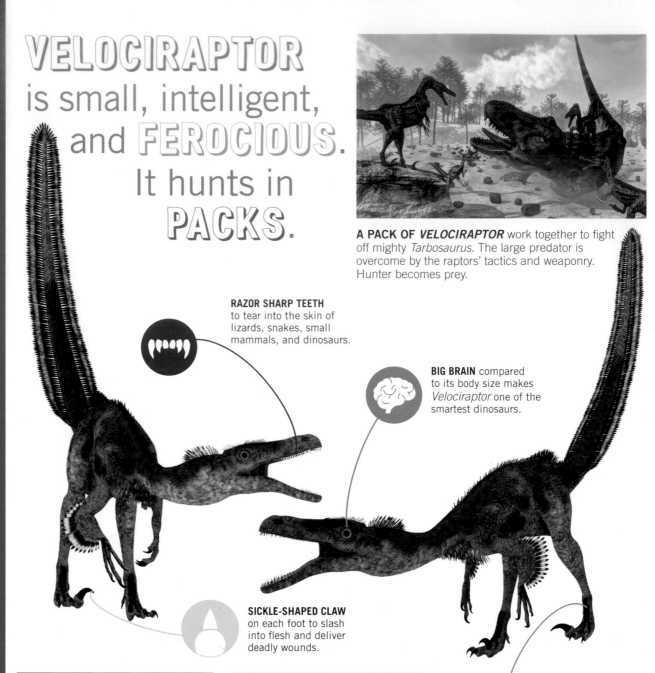

A PACK OF VELOCIRAPTOR work together to fight off mighty *Tarbosaurus*. The large predator is overcome by the raptors' tactics and weaponry. Hunter becomes prey.

RAZOR SHARP TEETH to tear into the skin of lizards, snakes, small mammals, and dinosaurs.

BIG BRAIN compared to its body size makes *Velociraptor* one of the smartest dinosaurs.

SICKLE-SHAPED CLAW on each foot to slash into flesh and deliver deadly wounds.

STRONG, SPEEDY LEGS to zip along in the sandy desert at 25 miles per hour.

ID KIT

VELOCIRAPTOR

(ve-LOSS-i-RAP-tor)

MEANING quick thief

FOSSILS FOUND Mongolia

WHEN Late Cretaceous

LENGTH 6 feet

WEIGHT up to 33 pounds

DIET carnivore

FOOD other animals

These CLUES will help you to find where the *VELOCIRAPTORS* are hiding in this book:

 Pack hunters. **Find more than one** *Velociraptor*.

 Sharp claws to eat meat. Look for prey, such as *Protoceratops*.

 Prey to larger predators. **Look for** *Tarbosaurus*.

 Now turn to the GLOW-IN-THE-DARK habitat pages to catch a *VELOCIRAPTOR*!

SHEEP-SIZE *PROTOCERATOPS* puts up a good fight against a single *Velociraptor*. It can grip and bite with its sharp beak. But it doesn't stand a chance against a pack.

STEGOSAURUS has HUGE bony plates on its back and four DEADLY SPIKES on its tail.

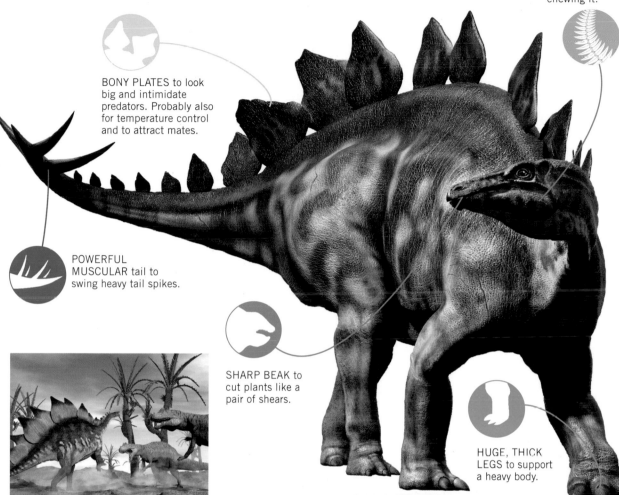

CHEEK POUCHES to store food before chewing it.

BONY PLATES to look big and intimidate predators. Probably also for temperature control and to attract mates.

POWERFUL MUSCULAR tail to swing heavy tail spikes.

SHARP BEAK to cut plants like a pair of shears.

HUGE, THICK LEGS to support a heavy body.

STEGOSAURUS is the size of a truck. Its tail spikes can pierce open the flesh of an attacker. But *Stegosaurus* is slow and doesn't have the wits of a predator like *Allosaurus*. Who will win this battle?

A FOREST CLEARING is the perfect place for *Stegosaurus* to forage on low-lying forest plants such as ferns and mosses. It has a short neck, so can't reach up to high branches.

ID KIT

STEGOSAURUS

(STEG-oh-SORE-rus)

MEANING roof lizard

FOSSILS FOUND USA

WHEN Late Jurassic

LENGTH 29.5 feet

WEIGHT 5-7 tons

DIET herbivore

FOOD low-lying plants

These **CLUES** will help you to find where *STEGOSAURUS* is hiding in this book:

Sharp beak to cut tough plants. **Look for conifers and other vegetation.**

Prey to big dinosaurs. **Look for *Allosaurus*.**

Short neck means low-lying plant eater. **Find ferns and mosses.**

Now turn to the GLOW-IN-THE-DARK habitat pages to catch a *STEGOSAURUS*!

ICHTHYOSAURS look like dolphins but swim like sharks. Their long, thin snouts SNAP UP fish.

 HUGE, FLAT EYES—up to ten inches across—can spot prey in dark, deep waters.

 STREAMLINED SNOUT and body for high speed and mobility.

 SHARP, NEEDLE-LIKE TEETH to catch fast-moving fish, squid and shell-fish.

 FORE-FINS to maneuver during swimming.

ID KIT

ICHTHYOSAUR

(ICK-thee-oh-SORE)

MEANING fish lizard

FOSSILS FOUND Europe

WHEN Mesozoic Era

LENGTH 2-49 feet

WEIGHT 2-200 pounds

DIET carnivore

FOOD fish, squid, shell-fish

These **CLUES** will help you to find where the *ICHTHYOSAURS* are hiding in this book:

 Huge eyes to see in dark waters. **Find deep water.**

 Needle-like teeth to catch fast-moving prey. **Look for fish.**

 Hunt in groups. **Search for a pod.**

Now turn to the GLOW-IN-THE-DARK habitat pages to catch an *ICHTHYOSAUR*!

ICHTHYOSAURS HUNT IN PODS, or groups, like modern-day dolphins. They work together to herd schools of fish into tight balls, or to chase them into shallow waters.

12

DORSAL FIN for stability.

LEAPING AT GREAT SPEED, an *ichthyosaur* breaks the water to breathe air into its lungs. *Ichthyosaurs* can't breathe under water like fish because they don't have gills.

POWERFUL TAIL FINS whip quickly from side to side for speedy swimming.

SMALL *ICHTHYOSAURS* aren't safe from predators. When they lived 90-250 million years ago, *ichthyosaurs* were preyed on by *Kronosaurus*. This huge pliosaur had a large head and a short muscular neck, perfect for tearing apart prey.

ANKYLOSAURUS
is a slow-moving plant eater. It is built like a **TANK**.

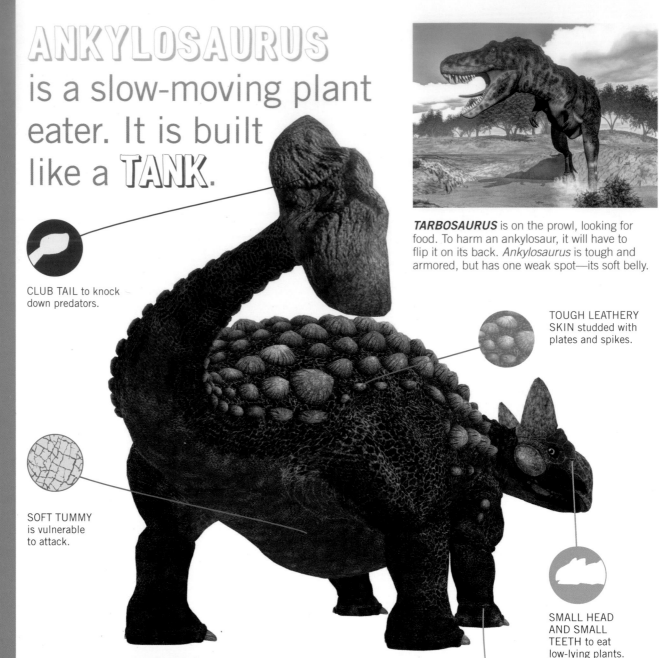

CLUB TAIL to knock down predators.

SOFT TUMMY is vulnerable to attack.

TARBOSAURUS is on the prowl, looking for food. To harm an ankylosaur, it will have to flip it on its back. *Ankylosaurus* is tough and armored, but has one weak spot—its soft belly.

TOUGH LEATHERY SKIN studded with plates and spikes.

SMALL HEAD AND SMALL TEETH to eat low-lying plants.

THICK, STOCKY LEGS to support a heavy, bulky body.

ID KIT

ANKYLOSAURUS

(an-KIE-loh-sore-us)

MEANING stiff lizard

FOSSILS FOUND Canada, USA

WHEN Late Cretaceous

LENGTH 33 feet

WEIGHT 5.5 tons

DIET herbivore

FOOD grasses, shrubs

These CLUES will help you to find where *ANKYLOSAURUS* is hiding in this book:

 Small teeth to eat plants. **Look for vegetation.**

 Small head and short neck means low-lying plants. **Find grasses and shrubs.**

 A swinging club tail shouldn't be too hard to spot! **Look for this feature.**

 Now turn to the GLOW-IN-THE-DARK habitat pages to catch an *ANKYLOSAURUS*!

A CLUB TAIL is a deadly weapon. Used like a wrecking ball, it can swing like a sledge-hammer and seriously damage an attacking predator.

PTEROSAURS fly through the air on bat-like WINGS.

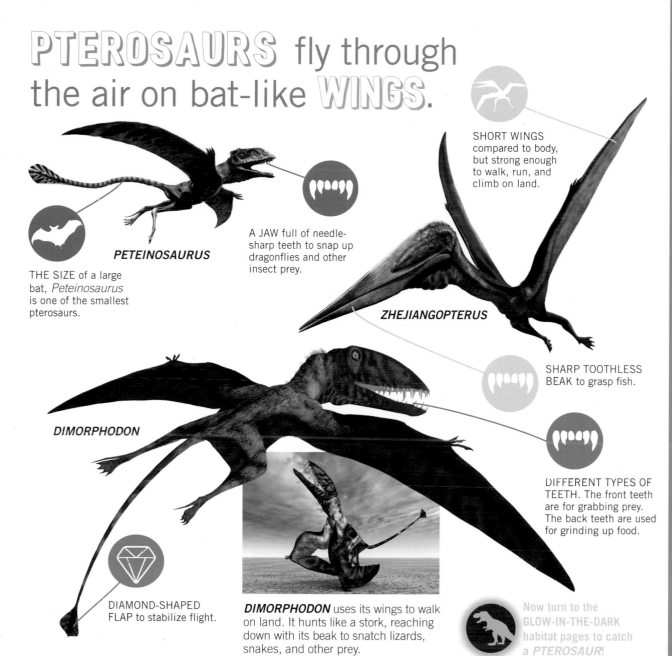

PETEINOSAURUS

THE SIZE of a large bat, *Peteinosaurus* is one of the smallest pterosaurs.

A JAW full of needle-sharp teeth to snap up dragonflies and other insect prey.

SHORT WINGS compared to body, but strong enough to walk, run, and climb on land.

ZHEJIANGOPTERUS

SHARP TOOTHLESS BEAK to grasp fish.

DIMORPHODON

DIFFERENT TYPES OF TEETH. The front teeth are for grabbing prey. The back teeth are used for grinding up food.

DIAMOND-SHAPED FLAP to stabilize flight.

DIMORPHODON uses its wings to walk on land. It hunts like a stork, reaching down with its beak to snatch lizards, snakes, and other prey.

Now turn to the **GLOW-IN-THE-DARK** habitat pages to catch a *PTEROSAUR*!

ID KIT

PETEINOSAURUS

(pe-TY-ne-SORE-us)

MEANING winged lizard

FOSSILS FOUND Italy

WHEN Late Triassic

WINGSPAN 24 inches

WEIGHT 3.5 ounces

DIET insectivore

FOOD insects

CLUE

 Eats insects. **Look for dragonflies.**

ID KIT

DIMORPHODON

(dye-MOF-o-don)

MEANING two-formed tooth

FOSSILS FOUND Europe, USA

WHEN Early Jurassic

WINGSPAN 4.6 feet

WEIGHT 2 pounds

DIET carnivore

FOOD insects, small reptiles

CLUE

 Eats small reptiles. **Look for lizards and snakes.**

ID KIT

ZHEJIANGOPTERUS

(zhe-zang-OP-ter-us)

MEANING Zhejiang wing

FOSSILS FOUND China

WHEN Late Cretaceous

WINGSPAN 11.5 feet

WEIGHT 50-75 pounds

DIET carnivore

FOOD fish

CLUE

Eats fish. **Find a stretch of water that it can dive into.**

WOOLLY MAMMOTHS use their enormous TUSKS to dig for food in the SNOW and fight off predators and rivals.

THICK WOOLLY COAT for living in a cold climate.

SHORT TAIL to conserve heat.

SNOW isn't a problem for the woolly mammoth, designed for life in a cold climate. The mammoth's thick, woolly coat has two layers—a long, coarse outer coat and a short, dense undercoat. Its short tail and small ears help to conserve heat. Its huge tusks scrape away snow and ice to find shrubs, grasses, and roots to eat.

ID KIT

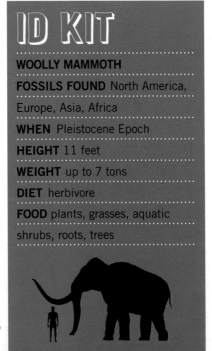

WOOLLY MAMMOTH

FOSSILS FOUND North America, Europe, Asia, Africa

WHEN Pleistocene Epoch

HEIGHT 11 feet

WEIGHT up to 7 tons

DIET herbivore

FOOD plants, grasses, aquatic shrubs, roots, trees

These **CLUES** will help you to find where THE WOOLLY MAMMOTH is hiding in this book:

 Sharp tusks to fight off predators. **Look for** *Smilodon.*

 Adapted to a cold environment. **Find snow and ice.**

 Woolly mammoths stay away from hunting humans. **Look for an uninhabited area.**

 Now turn to the GLOW-IN-THE-DARK habitat pages to catch a WOOLLY MAMMOTH!

A BABY MAMMOTH stays close to its mother. She feeds it with her own milk, and protects it from danger. Mothers and babies live in a group. If a mother dies, another will adopt its calf.

TUSKS, up to 14 feet long, to dig in the ground for food, and fight one another for territory and mating.

SMALL EARS to cut body heat loss.

TRUNK with two finger-like projections for feeding on tundra shrubs.

FOUR GIANT TEETH to grind up vegetation. Mammoths grow six sets of teeth over their lifetime, which is usually 60-80 years.

HUMANS moved into woolly mammoth habitats around 40,000 years ago. They hunted these mammals for meat, bones, and skin. At this time, woolly mammoths were also attacked by *Smilodon* and other large Ice Age predators.

SWAMP CLUES

water crocodiles fish trees panthers

MEGALODON

CATCH ME if you can!

MEGALODON is the biggest shark ever. It is three times longer than **A GREAT WHITE.**

GILLS for breathing underwater.

FLEXIBLE FINS for steering.

MEGALODON has the most powerful bite of any animal that's ever lived. These striped dolphins don't stand a chance.

EXCELLENT SENSE OF SMELL to detect prey in the water.

GIGANTIC JAWS up to 11 feet across and 9 feet high. That's big enough to swallow a school bus with room to spare!

MORE THAN 250 giant teeth, each up to 7 inches across.

ID KIT

MEGALODON (MEG-ah-low-don)

MEANING big tooth

FOSSILS FOUND Africa, North & South America, Europe, Asia, Australia

WHEN Late Oligocene to Early Pleistocene

LENGTH 60 feet

WEIGHT 66 tons

DIET carnivore

FOOD sharks, whales, seals, dolphins

These CLUES will help you to find where MEGALODON is hiding in this book:

Fins and gills for living underwater. **Find an ocean.**

A bloodthirsty carnivore. **Look for large underwater prey.**

Monsterous size. **You won't miss it!**

Now turn to the GLOW-IN-THE-DARK habitat pages to catch a MEGALODON!

LIVYATAN is a 50-foot sperm whale from 9-10 million years ago. It hunted whales and seals, and battled with *Megalodon* for prey. In combat, *Megalodon* bit off the whale's fins so that it couldn't swim away.

ALLOSAURUS is a big, fierce hunter that preys on other SUPERSIZED dinosaurs.

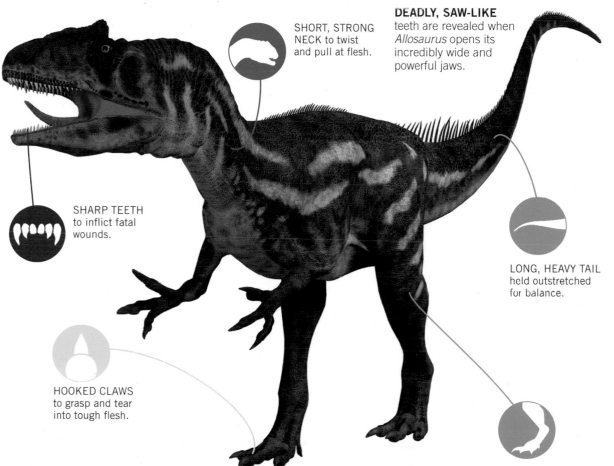

DEADLY, SAW-LIKE teeth are revealed when *Allosaurus* opens its incredibly wide and powerful jaws.

SHORT, STRONG NECK to twist and pull at flesh.

SHARP TEETH to inflict fatal wounds.

LONG, HEAVY TAIL held outstretched for balance.

HOOKED CLAWS to grasp and tear into tough flesh.

LONG HIND LEGS for running fast. It can travel up to 20 mph.

ID KIT

ALLOSAURUS

(AL-oh-SORE-us)

MEANING other lizard

FOSSILS FOUND Portugal, USA

WHEN Late Jurassic

LENGTH 39 feet

WEIGHT up to 3 tons

DIET carnivore

FOOD other dinosaurs

These **CLUES** will help you to find where *ALLOSAURUS* is hiding in this book:

 Preys on big dinosaurs. **Look for** *Stegosaurus*.

 Lives in forests, but is too big to be amongst the trees. **Search for a forest clearing.**

 Colossal, gaping jaws. **Look for this feature.**

 Now turn to the **GLOW-IN-THE-DARK** habitat pages to catch an *ALLOSAURUS*!

ALLOSAURUS preys on big dinosaurs such as *Stegosaurus*. It might also attack a sauropod, but it takes more than one *Allosaurus* to bring such a gigantic dinosaur down.

DESERT CLUES

rocks sand lizards snakes desert plants

MICRORAPTOR is one of the smallest dinosaurs. It CLIMBS trees and glides through the air.

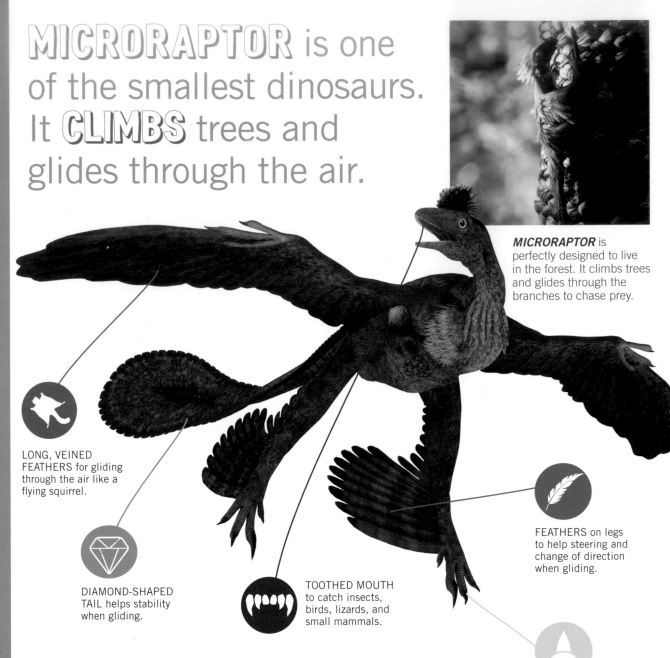

MICRORAPTOR is perfectly designed to live in the forest. It climbs trees and glides through the branches to chase prey.

LONG, VEINED FEATHERS for gliding through the air like a flying squirrel.

DIAMOND-SHAPED TAIL helps stability when gliding.

TOOTHED MOUTH to catch insects, birds, lizards, and small mammals.

FEATHERS on legs to help steering and change of direction when gliding.

CLAWS for climbing trees.

ID KIT

MICRORAPTOR

(MIKE-row-rap-tor)

MEANING tiny thief

FOSSILS FOUND China

WHEN Early Cretaceous

LENGTH 16 inches

WEIGHT 2.2 pounds

DIET carnivore

FOOD lizards, small mammals, insects

These **CLUES** will help you to find where *MICRORAPTOR* is hiding in this book:

 Claws for climbing. **Look for forest trees.**

 Teeth for eating prey. **Look for lizards such as *Xianglong*.**

 Wings for gliding. It won't be on the ground.

 Now turn to the GLOW-IN-THE-DARK habitat pages to catch a *MICRORAPTOR*!

XIANGLONG is a flying lizard from the Early Cretaceous. It scampers up trees and glides through the forest to escape the jaws of its predator, *Microraptor*.

MAIASAURA lives in large herds. It builds NESTS and looks after its young.

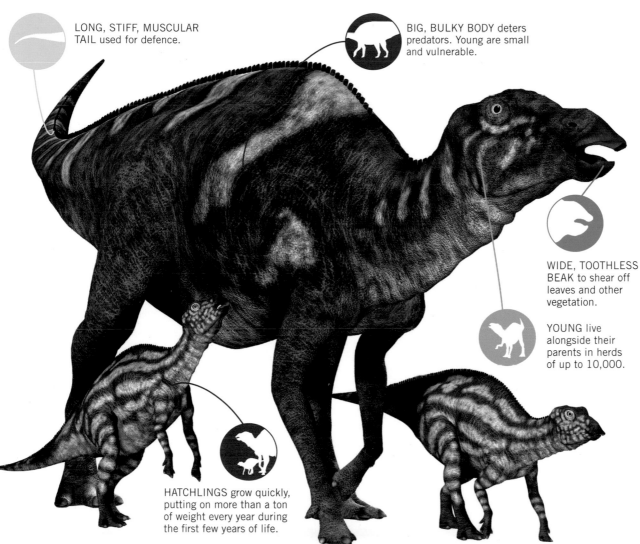

LONG, STIFF, MUSCULAR TAIL used for defence.

BIG, BULKY BODY deters predators. Young are small and vulnerable.

WIDE, TOOTHLESS BEAK to shear off leaves and other vegetation.

YOUNG live alongside their parents in herds of up to 10,000.

HATCHLINGS grow quickly, putting on more than a ton of weight every year during the first few years of life.

TROODON raids *Maiasaura* nesting sites for eggs and young. This small, fast-moving killer is smart. It has a keen sense of smell, acute hearing, and large forward-facing eyes to hunt at night.

ID KIT

MAIASAURA

(my-ah-SORE-ah)

MEANING good mother lizard

FOSSILS FOUND USA

WHEN Late Cretaceous

LENGTH up to 30 feet

WEIGHT 5 tons

DIET herbivore

FOOD plants

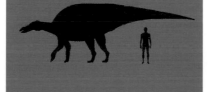

These CLUES will help you to find where the *MAIASAURA* are hiding in this book:

Toothless beak and cheek teeth mean herbivore. **Look for plants.**

Hatchlings live with parents. **Look for a mother with her young.**

Young *Maisaura* are easy targets for large meat-eaters. **Look for big predators.**

Now turn to the GLOW-IN-THE-DARK habitat pages to catch the *MAIASAURA!*

OCEAN CLUES

deep water   fish   whales   squid   shellfish

DIPLODOCUS uses its long neck to reach treetop leaves. Its SUPERSONIC tail lashes out at attackers.

LONG TAIL for counterbalancing an extraordinarily long neck.

PREDATORS are put off by *Diplodocus's* vast size. But it doesn't always stop them. Fierce, bulky meat-eaters such as *Ceratosaurus* will attack. *Diplodocus* uses its long neck and tail to strike back. It may also lash out with its sharp "thumb" claws.

A WHIPPING TAIL is used to fend off predators. *Diplodocus's* tail is supersonic, which means it can travel faster than the speed of sound. A sonic boom, or explosive sound, is made as it cracks through the air.

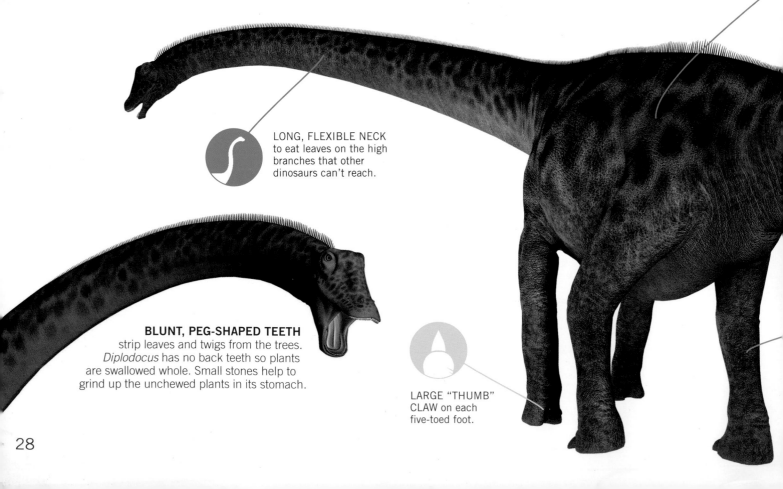

LONG, FLEXIBLE NECK to eat leaves on the high branches that other dinosaurs can't reach.

BLUNT, PEG-SHAPED TEETH strip leaves and twigs from the trees. *Diplodocus* has no back teeth so plants are swallowed whole. Small stones help to grind up the unchewed plants in its stomach.

LARGE "THUMB" CLAW on each five-toed foot.

DIPLODOCUS REACHES its long neck into the trees to feed like a modern giraffe. It doesn't have to move the rest of its body very much, which saves precious energy. This huge dinosaur needs to eat for up to 20 hours a day to maintain its massive body size.

IT IS SAFER to live and travel in a herd. *Diplodocus* young travel in the center, surrounded by the large adults for protection. Predatory dinosaurs try to separate the young and the old and the weak from the rest of the group.

TOUGH SMOOTH SCALES protect *Diplodocus's* skin from injury.

THICK, PILLAR-LIKE LEGS support *Diplodocus's* huge body. It moves very slowly.

ID KIT

DIPLODOCUS

(DIP-low-DOCK-us)

MEANING double beam

FOSSILS FOUND USA

WHEN Late Jurassic

LENGTH 90 feet

WEIGHT up to 16 tons

DIET herbivore

FOOD leaves, soft plants

These **CLUES** will help you to find where a *DIPLODOCUS* **HERD** is hiding in this book:

 Long neck to eat leaves from high branches. **Look for tall trees.**

 Travels in herds. **Find a group of** *Diplodocus*.

 Lashing tail. **Listen for supersonic, whipping sounds.**

 Now turn to the GLOW-IN-THE-DARK habitat pages to catch a *DIPLODOCUS*!

FOREST CLUES

ferns   moss   conifer trees   lizards   small mammals

TYRANNOSAURUS REX

lunges at prey with open jaws. Its **58 TEETH** are as sharp as razors and the **SIZE** of bananas.

A KEEN SENSE OF SMELL helps *Tyrannosaurus rex* hunt live prey and to sniff out carrion, the flesh of a dead animal. *T. rex* uses its powerful neck muscles to throw its head back and toss the meat to the back of its mouth. Flesh and bone is swallowed whole.

POWERFUL JAWS can kill and eat almost any animal that comes its way.

RAZOR-SHARP TEETH, each up to nine inches long.

SHORT, STRONG ARMS with large claws to slash and wound prey.

BIRD-LIKE FEET with three, strong, forward-pointing toes, and a small toe at the back.

ID KIT

TYRANNOSAURUS REX

(Tie-RAN-oh-sore-us recks)

MEANING tyrant lizard

FOSSILS FOUND Canada, USA

WHEN Late Cretaceous

LENGTH 40 feet

WEIGHT 9 tons

DIET carnivore

FOOD other animals, carrion

These **CLUES** will help you to find where *TYRANNOSAURUS REX* is hiding in this book:

 A hungry carnivore with a big appetite. **Find lots of prey.**

 Sniffs out carrion. **Look for meat and left-overs.**

 Hunts day and night. **Look for somewhere that is populated at any time.**

 Now turn to the **GLOW-IN-THE-DARK** habitat pages to catch a *TYRANNOSAURUS REX!*

FRONT-FACING EYES for stereoscopic vision. *T. rex* has good eyesight and can judge distances well.

KEEN SENSE OF SMELL to hunt day and night.

***TYRANNOSAURUS REX* DOESN'T ALWAYS HUNT ALONE.** Sometimes, it hunts in packs. Two or more *T. rex* are more likely to bring down a big armored dinosaur such as *Triceratops*.

HEAVY TAIL to balance large body and head.

LARGE LEGS can move quickly in short bursts.

THIS PREDATOR'S TEETH are designed for different jobs. Its front teeth grip, its side teeth tear, and its back teeth dice. Chunks of flesh are then forced down its throat. *T. rex* can swallow a small dinosaur in one gulp.

TYRANNOSAURUS REX

SAVANNA CLUES

tall trees   grasses   shrubs   lizards   snakes

CORYTHOSAURUS
hoots through its crest
when there is DANGER.

STANDING ON TWO LEGS helps *Corythosaurus* reach the juicy leaves on high branches. It stands on four legs to browse low-lying vegetation.

HOLLOW, BONY CREST for making hooting sounds. *Corythosaurus* blows air through the hollow tubes in its crest.

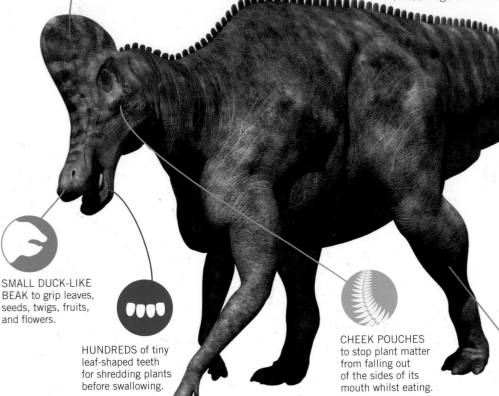

LONG TAIL with strong connecting tissue to prevent it from drooping.

SMALL DUCK-LIKE BEAK to grip leaves, seeds, twigs, fruits, and flowers.

HUNDREDS of tiny leaf-shaped teeth for shredding plants before swallowing.

CHEEK POUCHES to stop plant matter from falling out of the sides of its mouth whilst eating.

LARGE HIND LEGS for running on two legs.

ID KIT

CORYTHOSAURUS

(koh-rith-OH-sore-us)

MEANING helmet lizard

FOSSILS FOUND Canada, USA

WHEN Late Cretaceous

LENGTH 33 feet

WEIGHT 4 tons

DIET herbivore

FOOD plants

These CLUES will help you to find where *CORYTHOSAURUS* is hiding in this book:

 Small beak to grip delicate plants. **Look for flowers and shrubs.**

 Lives in herds. **Find more than one *Corythosaurus*.**

 Bony crest used for communication. **Listen for hooting sounds.**

 Now turn to the **GLOW-IN-THE-DARK** habitat pages to catch a *CORYTHOSAURUS*!

LIVING IN HERDS means safety in numbers. Many eyes can look out for predators such as *T. rex* and *Albertosaurus*. *Corythosaurus* warn each other of danger by hooting through their bony crests.

LIOPLEURODON
ambushes prey at high SPEED in the ocean depths.

POWERFUL FLIPPERS push *Liopleurodon's* massive body through the water, allowing it to accelerate quickly as it ambushes prey. It is a deadly ocean predator.

STRONG SENSE OF SMELL to detect prey in dark waters.

LARGE HEAD and short, strong neck.

LONG, POINTED TEETH for grabbing prey and tearing through flesh, bone, and muscle.

FOUR PADDLE-LIKE limbs for powerful swimming.

ID KIT

LIOPLEURODON

(Lie-oh-ploor-oh-don)

MEANING smooth-sided teeth

FOSSILS FOUND Europe

WHEN Mid to Late Jurassic

LENGTH up to 21 feet

WEIGHT 1–1.7 tons

DIET carnivore

FOOD pliosaurs, ichthyosaurs, marine crocodiles, ammonites

These CLUES will help you to find where *LIOPLEURODON* is hiding in this book:

 Large, powerful swimmer. **Find an ocean.**

 Preys on large sea creatures. **Look for whales and icthyosaurs.**

 Huge, teeth-filled jaws. **Look for this feature.**

 Now turn to the GLOW-IN-THE-DARK habitat pages to catch a *LIOPLEURODON*!

LIOPLEURODON'S vast, powerful jaws are full of long, pointed teeth for grabbing prey. It feasts on ichthyosaurs, pliosaurs, and other large sea creatures.

PARK CLUES

flowers   leaves   shrubs   dragonflies   ferns

SMILODON
uses its powerful forelimbs to pull down large prey. It delivers a **LETHAL BITE** to the throat.

SHARP SABRE TEETH for stabbing and slashing flesh.

POWERFUL JAWS can open 120 degrees.

SMILODON'S LONG, SABRE TEETH are the size of large kitchen knives. They are used for stabbing vulnerable, fleshy parts of prey such as the neck.

ID KIT

SMILODON (SMAHY-luh-don)

COMMON NAME sabre-toothed tiger

FOSSILS FOUND North, South, and Central America

WHEN Pleistocene

LENGTH up to 7.5 feet

WEIGHT up to 880 pounds

DIET carnivore

FOOD large herbivores

These **CLUES** will help you to find where the *SMILODON* are hiding in this book:

Thick fur to survive the Ice Age. **Find a cold climate.**

Lives and hunts in packs. **Look for a group.**

Hunts large herbivores. **Look for a woolly mammoth.**

Now turn to the GLOW-IN-THE-DARK habitat pages to catch a *SMILIDON*!

POWERFUL FORELIMBS to pull down prey and pin it to the ground.

LONG, RETRACTABLE CLAWS for spearing prey and holding onto a victim to bring it down.

MUSCULAR NECK gives *Smilodon* the power to stab and slash its victim's throat with its teeth.

SMILODON hunts live prey, but also scavenges left-overs. It rips open flesh with its long sabre teeth, but can't bite into bone because its teeth are likely to break—they are sharp, but not very strong.

MUSCULAR BODY perfectly designed to ambush large prey.

BISON, HORSES, AND WOOLLY MAMMOTHS are all on *Smilodon's* dinner menu. Its powerful forelimbs are strong enough to hold down a hefty herbivore while delivering a killing bite.

LIKE A MODERN LION, *Smilodon* might live and hunt in pack to stalk prey. A pack works together to separate the young and the weak, which are less able to defend themselves.

41

ARCTIC TUNDRA CLUES

snow ice musk ox grasses roots

QUETZALCOATLUS is wider than some JET FIGHTER planes. It EATS small dinosaurs.

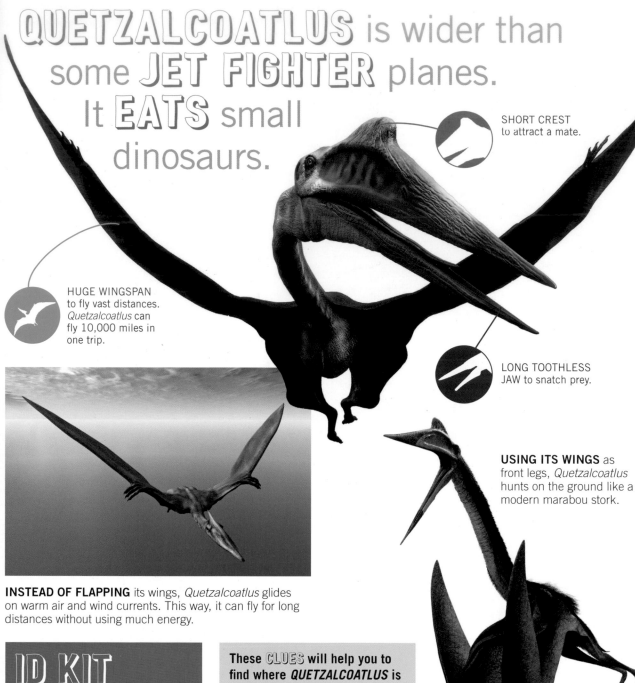

SHORT CREST
to attract a mate.

HUGE WINGSPAN
to fly vast distances.
Quetzalcoatlus can
fly 10,000 miles in
one trip.

LONG TOOTHLESS
JAW to snatch prey.

USING ITS WINGS as
front legs, *Quetzalcoatlus*
hunts on the ground like a
modern marabou stork.

INSTEAD OF FLAPPING its wings, *Quetzalcoatlus* glides
on warm air and wind currents. This way, it can fly for long
distances without using much energy.

ID KIT

QUETZALCOATLUS

(KWET-zal-koh-AT-las)

MEANING serpent god

FOSSILS FOUND USA

WHEN Late Cretaceous

WINGSPAN 38 feet

WEIGHT 550 pounds

DIET carnivore

FOOD anything smaller than it is

These **CLUES** will help you to
find where *QUETZALCOATLUS* is
hiding in this book:

 Flies for long
distances.
Look up into the sky.

 Snatches prey with
its beak. **Look for
small dinosaurs, other
animals, and carrion.**

 Huge wingspan
You can't miss it!

 Now turn to the
GLOW-IN-THE-DARK
habitat pages to catch a
QUETZALCOATLUS!

QUETZALCOATLUS reaches down
with its beak to snatch lizards, snakes,
eggs, mammals, and small dinosaurs.
It will eat anything that is smaller than
it is, and carrion, too.

TRICERATOPS uses its three DEADLY HORNS to ward off predators.

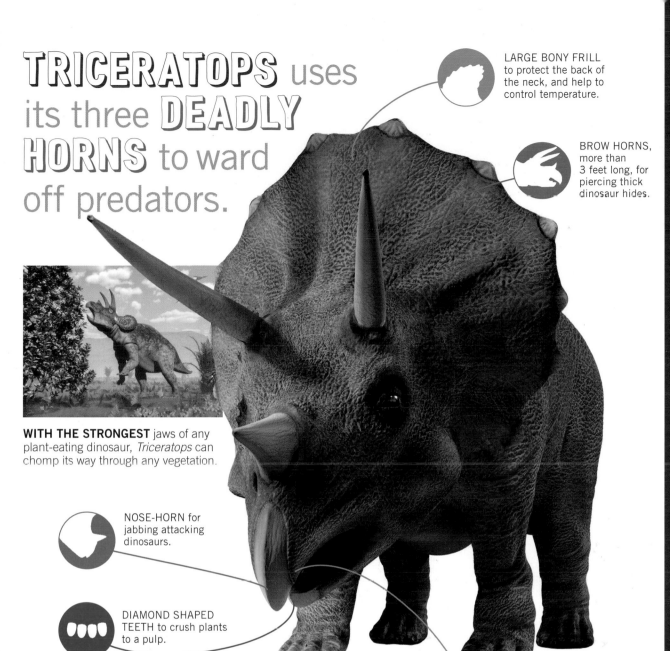

LARGE BONY FRILL to protect the back of the neck, and help to control temperature.

BROW HORNS, more than 3 feet long, for piercing thick dinosaur hides.

WITH THE STRONGEST jaws of any plant-eating dinosaur, *Triceratops* can chomp its way through any vegetation.

NOSE-HORN for jabbing attacking dinosaurs.

DIAMOND SHAPED TEETH to crush plants to a pulp.

BEAK-LIKE MOUTH to tear vegetation.

ID KIT

TRICERATOPS

(tri-SERRA-tops)

MEANING three-horned face

FOSSILS FOUND USA

WHEN Late Cretaceous

LENGTH 30 feet

WEIGHT 6 tons

DIET herbivore

FOOD tough plants

These CLUES will help you to find where *TRICERATOPS* is hiding in this book:

 Strong jaws to chomp through any vegetation. **Find trees, shrubs, and other plants.**

 Large neck frill. **Look for this feature.**

 Three big horns. **Look for this feature.**

 Now turn to the GLOW-IN-THE-DARK habitat pages to catch a *TRICERATOPS*!

TRICERATOPS can put up a good fight. If a predator such as *T. rex* attacks, *Triceratops* will charge and stab it with its sharp horns. Its thick frill helps to protect it from ferocious teeth.

46

CITY CLUES

DID YOU CATCH THEM?

Did you find the glow-in-the dark dinosaurs and prehistoric beasts?
Check the pictures below to make sure that you found them all.

Spinosaurus stalks the swamp looking for giant crocodiles. *Saurosuchus* lunges out of the water. Who will eat who? *Zhenjiangopterus* flies overhead, ready to dive for fish.

A pack of *Velociraptor* followed *Protoceratops* into the desert, and circles its prey. But hungry *Tarbosaurus* has followed them all. Who will get away?

A pod of ichthyosaurs hunt fish in the ocean depths. *Liopleurodon* has smelt the ichthyosaurs, and is ready to ambush. Mighty *Megalodon* is looking for lunch, too.

Stegosaurus browses moss and ferns in the forest clearing. It hasn't yet spotted deadly *Allosaurus*. *Microraptor* glides overhead chasing the flying lizard, *Xianglong*.

A herd of *Diplodocus* feed on the topmost branches of the savanna trees. *Ankylosaurus* grazes the grassland, and *Dimorphodon* scans the ground for lizards and snakes.

Corythosaurus nibbles on delicate flowers in the park. *Triceratops* chomps its way through shrubs and trees. *Peteinosaurus* snaps up dragonflies and other insects.

The woolly mammoth and her calf have found the snowy Arctic tundra. They were followed by a pack of hungry *Smilodon*. Can the mammoth mother save her calf?

Maiasaura and her young have wandered into New York City. *Quetzalcoatlus* targets a calf for lunch. Will *T. rex* feast on *Maiasaura* or the humans, or just scavenge for leftovers?